Snappy Learner

Spelling
ages 5-7

www.alligatorbooks.co.uk

© 2019 Alligator Products Limited
Published in 2019 by Alligator Products Limited, 2nd Floor, 314 Regents Park Road, London N3 2JX
The Alligator logo is a registered trade mark of Alligator Products Limited.
Printed in China.0947

Alphabet spelling

The alphabet has 26 letters. Write in the first letter of each picture to spell the word.

__pple

__ell

__amel

__inosaur

__lephant

__rog

__oat

__and

__ce-cream

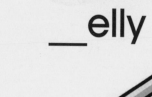

__elly

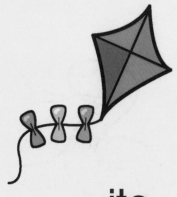

__ite

__adder

__onkey

Excellent! Stick a star sticker on your reward chart.

__ine

__range

__irate

__ueen

__obot

__nake

__ree

__mbrella

__an

__itch

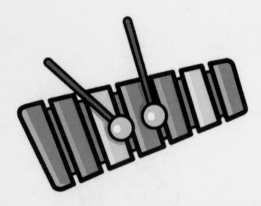

__ylophone

__o-yo

__ebra

Stick your Snappy Learner sticker here.

Well done!

Excellent! Stick a star sticker on your reward chart.

Finish the spelling

Each of these pictures is missing the last letter of the word. Write in the last letter to complete the word.

he__

fla__

tomat__

ow__

an__

rin__

co__

feathe__

clow__

shee__

ca__

lea__

robi__

Stick your Snappy Learner sticker here.

Well done!

Excellent! Stick a star sticker on your reward chart.

Let's learn to spell with vowels

The letters **aeiou** are called **vowels**. There is at least one vowel in most words. Look at the pictures and fill in the missing **a** in each word. Then read the word out loud. Can you hear the **a** sound?

c__ke

p__n

b__t

c__r

__rrow

m__n

Look at the pictures and fill in the missing **e** in each word. Then read the word out loud. Can you hear the **e** sound?

__ar

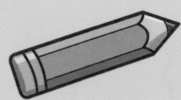

p__ncil

z__bra

__ight

k__y

b__d

Excellent! Stick a star sticker on your reward chart.

Look at the pictures and fill in the missing **i** in each word. Then read the word out loud. Can you hear the **i** sound?

__ce-cream

__sland

kn__ght

l__on

__ron

__gloo

Look at the pictures and fill in the missing **o** in each word. Then read the word out loud. Can you hear the **o** sound?

tomat__

__range

__wl

d__ll

d__g

Excellent! Stick a star sticker on your reward chart.

Look at the pictures and fill in the missing **u** in each word. Then read the word out loud. Can you hear the **u** sound?

c__p

b__s

octop__s

__mbrella

__nicorn

r__g

Consonant letters

The letters **aeiou** are called **vowels**. All the other letters are called **consonants**. How many vowels and how many consonants can you find in these words? Write the consonant letters on the line underneath the picture.

flower

_____

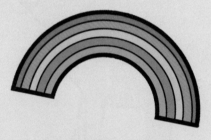

rainbow

_____

penguin

_____

knife

_____

tiger

_____

 Excellent! Stick a star sticker on your reward chart.

Stick your Snappy Learner sticker here.

Well done!

Double vowels

Some words have two vowels which are the same in them. Write the double vowels in the spaces to complete the words.

Double vowels: **aa ee ii oo uu**

d __ __ r

ball __ __ n

b __ __ k

sk __ __ ng

sh __ __ p

__ __ rdvark

Rhyming words

Many words sound similar and have similar endings. These are called **rhyming words**. Draw a line to join the words that rhyme.

Excellent! Stick a star sticker on your reward chart.

Change the letter

By simply changing one letter of a word, we can make a new word.
Read the words in the balloons and draw a line to the new word
made by changing one of the letters.

pen

rust

port

late

some

rake

soar

dear

part

gate

pin

wear

rest

bake

same

soap

Sounds similar

Some words rhyme but are spelt differently and have different meanings. Draw a line to the rhyming words on these bears.

 Excellent! Stick a star sticker on your reward chart.

Right & wrong

Read the words on the objects below. Tick the words that are spelt correctly and cross out the ones that are wrong.

Let's spell with toys

Write in the missing letters to spell the toys below.

te__d__   b__a__   j__ __-s__w

__ __ain   r__ll__ __   s__ate

f__ __ __tb__ll

Excellent! Stick a star sticker on your reward chart.

Find the hidden word

Some words have another word inside them. For instance the word SHOUT has the word **OUT** in it. Find and underline the hidden words in the clouds!

water

monkey

drink

elephant

orange

clown

tomato

bread

broom

towel

cloud

butterfly

Stick your Snappy Learner sticker here.

Well done!

Spelling test

See if you can spell these words with only one letter to help you.

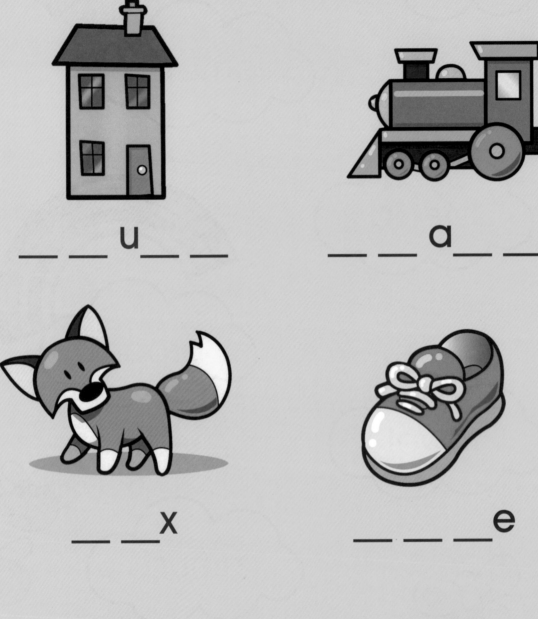

_ _ u _ _

_ _ a _ _

_ _ x

_ _ _ e

_ u _

_ _ v _

The letter e

The letter **e** is the most common letter of the alphabet. When we add **e** to the end of some words, it makes a new word. Add **e** to the end of these words. The first one has been done for you.

tap → tape

car

be

pin

man

cap

Excellent! Stick a star sticker on your reward chart.

Spelling time!

Look at the times on the clocks and then write your answer on the line underneath. Times always end with **o'clock**. Write **o'clock** after each number. The first one has been done for you.

one

two

<u>one o'clock</u>

_____

three

_____   _____

four

five

_____   _____

six

seven

eight

_____   _____

nine

ten

_____   _____

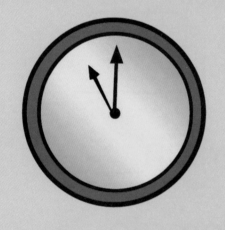

eleven

twelve

_____   _____

 Excellent! Stick a star sticker on your reward chart.

Stick your Snappy Learner sticker here.

Well done!

Plural words

When there is more than one of something it becomes a **plural**. Most words becomes **plural** simply by adding **s** or **es** to the end of a word. For example, a **chair** becomes **chairs** and a **box** becomes **boxes**. Write the letter **s** or **es** after each word below.

s	**es**
cat__	dress__ __
carrot__	hero__ __
window__	kiss__ __
table__	wish__ __
cake__	witch__ __
ladybird__	tomato__ __
sweet__	fox__ __
toy__	bus__ __

Some words that end in **y** become **ies** when plural. Write the letters **ies** after each word below.

ies

lady   ladies

daisy   dais__ __ __

family   famil__ __ __

story   stor__ __ __

berry   berr__ __ __

fairy   fair__ __ __

Stick your Snappy Learner sticker here.

Well done!

Excellent! Stick a star sticker on your reward chart.

Silent letters

Some words have silent letters, but they must be included to spell a word properly. Each of the pictures below has a silent letter missing.

Can you add the silent letter to the end of each word?
It could be **e b g h u** or **w**.

com__

lam__

thum__

hous__

cak__

mous__

__nome

__nat

si__n

ding__y

g__ost

sc__ool

bisc__it

g__itar

g__inea pig

2

t_o

__rist

 Excellent! Stick a star sticker on your reward chart.

Magic spelling!

Practise your spelling skills by adding the missing letters to all the words.

__anan__

__lephan__

cak__

__ite

__ __ __h

rab__ __ __

s__ __ __p

buc__ __ __

g__ __ __

f__ __ __er

__ __brell__

Excellent! Stick a star sticker on your reward chart.

Check your answers

Alphabet spelling

apple
bell
camel
dinosaur
elephant
frog
goat
hand
ice-cream
jelly
kite
ladder
monkey
nine
orange
pirate
queen
robot
snake
tree
umbrella
van
witch
xylophone
yo-yo
zebra

Finish the spelling

hen   flag   tomat**o**
ow**l**   ant   rin**g**
cow   feather
clow**n**   shee**p**
cat   leaf   robi**n**

Let's learn to spell with vowels

cake   pan   bat
car   arrow   man
ear   pencil   zebra
eight   key   bed
ice-cream   island
kight   lion   iron
igloo
tomato   **o**range
owl   doll   dog
cup   bus   octopus
umbrella   unicorn
rug

Consonant letters

flower
rainbow
penguin
knife
tiger

Double vowels

deer   ball**oo**n
b**oo**k   ski**i**ng
sheep   **aa**rdvark

Rhyming words

tree – bee
sheep – sleep
rake – cake
boat – coat
chair - hair

Change the letter

pen – pin
rust – rest
port – part
late – gate
some – same
rake – bake
dear – wear
soar – soap

Sounds similar

pear – hair
rose – doze
eye – pie
leaf – theif

Right & wrong

✓   ✗
bucket   bukit
table   taybul
snail   snayal
rain   rayn
cake   kake
apple   appall
duck   duk

Let's spell with toys

teddy bear
jig-s**aw**
train
roller sk**ate**
football

Find the hidden word

wa**t**er
monkey   mon**key**
drink   d**rink**
eleph**ant**
or**an**ge
clown   cl**own**
to**mat**o
bread
broom
towel
cloud
butterfly   butter**fly**

Spelling test

house
train
fox
shoe
sun
five

The letter e

tap – tape
car – care
be – bee
pin – pine
man – mane
cap – cape

Spelling time

one o'clock
two o'clock
three o'clock
four o'clock
five o'clock
six o'clock
seven o'clock
eight o'clock
nine o'clock
ten o'clock
eleven o'clock
twelve o'clock

Plural words

s
cat**s**
carrot**s**
window**s**
table**s**
cake**s**

ladybird**s**
sweet**s**
toy**s**
es
dress**es**
hero**es**
kiss**es**
wish**es**
witch**es**
tomato**es**
fox**es**
bus**es**
ies
lad**ies**
dais**ies**
famil**ies**
stor**ies**
berr**ies**
fair**ies**

Silent letters

com**b**
lam**b**
thum**b**
house
cake
mouse
gnome
gnat
si**g**n
din**g**hy
ghost
school
biscuit
guitar
guinea pig
two
wrist

Magic spelling!

banana
elephant
cake
kite
fish
ra**bb**it
sheep
bucket
gate
flower
umbrella